JAC

*ER*

# THE
# FOUR FUNDAMENTAL
# CONCEPTS OF
# PSYCHO-ANALYSIS

*based on an edition*

Edited by

JACQUES-ALAIN MILLER

Translated from the French by

ALAN SHERIDAN

PARASITIC VENTURES PRESS

Toronto

Parasitic Ventures Press


A Saprophagous book first issued in 2011.


Source text is the 1981 W.W. Norton paperback edition of Jacques Lacan's *The Four Fundamental Concepts of Psycho-analysis*, as edited by Jacques-Alain Miller and translated by Alan Sheridan. This is *not* an authorized edition.


Library and Archives Canada Cataloguing in Publication

Lacan, Jacques, 1901-1981
    Erratum of The four fundamental concepts of psycho-analysis / Jacques Lacan ; Jacques-Alain Miller, editor ; Alan Sheridan, translator.

    Translation of: Les quatre concepts fondamentaux de la psychanalyse, originally published as v. 11 of the author's Le séminaire de Jacques Lacan
    Includes index.
    ISBN 978-0-9813263-5-1


        1. Psychoanalysis. I. Miller, Jacques-Alain II. Sheridan, Alan III. Title.
    IV. Title: Four fundamental concepts of psycho-analysis.

BF173.L33 2011              150.19'5              C2010-908123-4




ISBN 978-0-9813263-5-1

*ERRATUM OF*

# THE
# FOUR FUNDAMENTAL
# CONCEPTS OF
# PSYCHO-ANALYSIS

# CONTENTS

# CONTENTS

## TO CONCLUDE

# PREFACE TO THE
# ENGLISH-LANGUAGE EDITION

When the space of a lapsus no longer carries any meaning (or interpretation), then only is one sure that one is in the unconscious. *One Knows.*

But one has only to be aware of the fact to find oneself outside it. There is no friendship there, in that space that supports this unconscious.

All I can do is tell the truth. No, that isn't so—I have missed it. There is no truth that, in passing through awareness, does not lie.

But one runs after is all the same. ...

# PREFACE

# PREFACE

# EDITOR'S NOTE

Our intention here was to be as unobtrusive as possible . . .

P. V. P.

*ERRATUM OF*

# THE
# FOUR FUNDAMENTAL
# CONCEPTS OF
# PSYCHO-ANALYSIS

# 1

# EXCOMMUNICATION

# EXCOMMUNICATION

# EXCOMMUNICATION

# EXCOMMUNICATION

# EXCOMMUNICATION

# EXCOMMUNICATION

# EXCOMMUNICATION

# EXCOMMUNICATION

# EXCOMMUNICATION

# EXCOMMUNICATION

# EXCOMMUNICATION

# EXCOMMUNICATION

# EXCOMMUNICATION

# The Unconscious and Repetition

# 2

# THE FREUDIAN UNCONSCIOUS
# AND OURS

# THE UNCONSCIOUS AND REPETITION

# THE FREUDIAN UNCONSCIOUS AND OURS

# THE UNCONSCIOUS AND REPETITION

# THE FREUDIAN UNCONSCIOUS AND OURS

# THE FREUDIAN UNCONSCIOUS AND OURS

# THE UNCONSCIOUS AND REPETITION

# THE FREUDIAN UNCONSCIOUS AND OURS

# THE UNCONSCIOUS AND REPETITION

# THE FREUDIAN UNCONSCIOUS AND OURS

# THE UNCONSCIOUS AND REPETITION

# 3

# OF THE SUBJECT
# OF CERTAINTY

# OF THE SUBJECT OF CERTAINTY

# THE UNCONSCIOUS AND REPETITION

# OF THE SUBJECT OF CERTAINTY

# THE UNCONSCIOUS AND REPETITION

# OF THE SUBJECT OF CERTAINTY

# THE UNCONSCIOUS AND REPETITION

# OF THE SUBJECT OF CERTAINTY

# 4

# OF THE NETWORK
# OF SIGNIFIERS

Try to read this chapter five, line by line, in some language other than French. Those who do not know German should read it in the English translation. You will find this translation — I say this in passing — quite entertaining. You will see, for example, that the translation of *instinct* for *Trieb*, and *instinctual* for *triebhaft* has so many drawbacks for the translator that, although it is maintained throughout quite uniformly — thus basing the whole edition on a complete misunderstanding, since *Trieb* and *instinct* have nothing in common — the discord becomes so impossible at one point that the implications of a sentence cannot be carried through by translating *Triebhaft* by *instinctual*. A footnote becomes necessary — *At the beginning of the next paragraph the word Trieb . . . is much more revealing of urgency than the word instinctual. Trieb gives you a kick in the arse, my friends* — quite different from so-called *instinct*. That's how psycho-analytic teaching is passed on!

# THE UNCONSCIOUS AND REPETITION

# 5

## TUCHÉ AND AUTOMATION

# THE UNCONSCIOUS AND REPETITION

# TUCHÉ AND AUTOMATON

# TUCHÉ AND AUTOMATON

# TUCHÉ AND AUTOMATON

# TUCHÉ AND AUTOMATON

# THE UNCONSCIOUS AND REPETITION

# TUCHÉ AND AUTOMATON

# OF THE GAZE AS
*Object Petit a*

# 6

# THE SPLIT BETWEEN THE EYE
# AND THE GAZE

# OF THE GAZE

# THE EYE AND THE GAZE

# OF THE GAZE

# THE EYE AND THE GAZE

# OF THE GAZE

# THE EYE AND THE GAZE

# OF THE GAZE

# THE EYE AND THE GAZE

# OF THE GAZE

# THE EYE AND THE GAZE

# OF THE GAZE

# 7

# ANAMORPHOSIS

# OF THE GAZE

# ANAMORPHOSIS

# OF THE GAZE

# ANAMORPHOSIS

# OF THE GAZE

# ANAMORPHOSIS

# OF THE GAZE

# ANAMORPHOSIS

# OF THE GAZE

# ANAMORPHOSIS

# OF THE GAZE

# 8

# THE LINE AND THE LIGHT

# OF THE GAZE

# THE LINE AND LIGHT

# OF THE GAZE

# THE LINE AND LIGHT

No doubt, in the depths of my eye, the picture is painted. The picture, certainly, is in my eye. But I am ~~not~~ in the picture.

# THE LINE AND LIGHT

# OF THE GAZE

# THE LINE AND LIGHT

# OF THE GAZE

# THE LINE AND LIGHT

# OF THE GAZE

# THE LINE AND LIGHT

# OF THE GAZE

# 9

## WHAT IS A PICTURE?

# OF THE GAZE

# WHAT IS A PICTURE?

# WHAT IS A PICTURE?

# OF THE GAZE

# WHAT IS A PICTURE?

# OF THE GAZE

# WHAT IS A PICTURE?

# OF THE GAZE

# WHAT IS A PICTURE?

# WHAT IS A PICTURE?

# OF THE GAZE

# WHAT IS A PICTURE?

The Transference and the Drive

# 10

## PRESENCE OF THE ANALYST

# THE TRANSFERENCE AND THE DRIVE

# PRESENCE OF THE ANALYST

# THE TRANSFERENCE AND THE DRIVE

# PRESENCE OF THE ANALYST

# PRESENCE OF THE ANALYST

# PRESENCE OF THE ANALYST

# PRESENCE OF THE ANALYST

# 11

## ANALYSIS AND TRUTH OR
## THE CLOSURE OF THE UNCONSCIOUS

# ANALYSIS AND TRUTH

# ANALYSIS AND TRUTH

# ANALYSIS AND TRUTH

# ANALYSIS AND TRUTH

# THE TRANSFERENCE AND THE DRIVE

# ANALYSIS AND TRUTH

# ANALYSIS AND TRUTH

# 12

## SEXUALITY IN THE DEFILES
## OF THE SIGNIFIER

# SEXUALITY

# SEXUALITY

# SEXUALITY

# THE TRANSFERENCE AND THE DRIVE

# SEXUALITY

# SEXUALITY

# 13

## THE DECONSTRUCTION
## OF THE DRIVE

# THE DECONSTRUCTION OF THE DRIVE

# THE DECONSTRUCTION OF THE DRIVE

# THE TRANSFERENCE AND THE DRIVE

# THE DECONSTRUCTION OF THE DRIVE

# THE TRANSFERENCE AND THE DRIVE

# THE DECONSTRUCTION OF THE DRIVE

# THE TRANSFERENCE AND THE DRIVE

# THE DECONSTRUCTION OF THE DRIVE

# THE TRANSFERENCE AND THE DRIVE

# THE DECONSTRUCTION OF THE DRIVE

# 14

## THE PARTIAL DRIVE
## AND ITS CIRCUIT

# THE PARTIAL DRIVE AND ITS CIRCUIT

# THE TRANSFERENCE AND THE DRIVE

# THE PARTIAL DRIVE AND ITS CIRCUIT

# THE PARTIAL DRIVE AND ITS CIRCUIT

# THE PARTIAL DRIVE AND ITS CIRCUIT

# THE TRANSFERENCE AND THE DRIVE

# THE PARTIAL DRIVE AND ITS CIRCUIT

# 15

## FROM LOVE TO THE LIBIDO

# FROM LOVE TO THE LIBIDO

# FROM LOVE TO THE LIBIDO

# THE TRANSFERENCE AND THE DRIVE

# FROM LOVE TO THE LIBIDO

# FROM LOVE TO THE LIBIDO

# FROM LOVE TO THE LIBIDO

# FROM LOVE TO THE LIBIDO

The Field of the Other
and back to the Transference

# 16

## THE SUBJECT AND THE OTHER: ALIENATION

# ALIENATION

# THE FIELD OF THE OTHER

# ALIENATION

# THE FIELD OF THE OTHER

# ALIENATION

# THE FIELD OF THE OTHER

# ALIENATION

# THE FIELD OF THE OTHER

# ALIENATION

# THE FIELD OF THE OTHER

# ALIENATION

# 17

## THE SUBJECT AND THE OTHER:
## APHANISIS

# APHANISIS

# THE FIELD OF THE OTHER

# APHANISIS

# THE FIELD OF THE OTHER

# APHANISIS

# THE FIELD OF THE OTHER

# APHANISIS

# THE FIELD OF THE OTHER

# APHANISIS

# THE FIELD OF THE OTHER

# APHANISIS

# APHANISIS

# 18

## OF THE SUBJECT
## WHO IS SUPPOSED TO KNOW,
## OF THE FIRST DYAD,
## AND OF THE GOOD

# OF THE SUBJECT WHO IS SUPPOSED TO KNOW

# THE FIELD OF THE OTHER

# THE FIELD OF THE OTHER

# THE FIELD OF THE OTHER

# THE FIELD OF THE OTHER

# OF THE SUBJECT WHO IS SUPPOSED TO KNOW

# OF THE SUBJECT WHO IS SUPPOSED TO KNOW

# THE FIELD OF THE OTHER

# 19

## FROM INTERPRETATION
## TO THE TRANSFERENCE

# THE FIELD OF THE OTHER

# FROM INTERPRETATION TO THE TRANSFERENCE

# THE FIELD OF THE OTHER

# THE FIELD OF THE OTHER

# THE FIELD OF THE OTHER

# THE FIELD OF THE OTHER

# THE FIELD OF THE OTHER

# THE FIELD OF THE OTHER

# To Conclude

# 20

## IN YOU MORE THAN YOU

# TO CONCLUDE

# IN YOU MORE THAN YOU

# TO CONCLUDE

# IN YOU MORE THAN YOU

# TO CONCLUDE

# IN YOU MORE THAN YOU

# TO CONCLUDE

# IN YOU MORE THAN YOU

# TO CONCLUDE

# IN YOU MORE THAN YOU

# TO CONCLUDE

# IN YOU MORE THAN YOU

# TO CONCLUDE

# TRANSLATOR'S NOTE

# TRANSLATOR'S NOTE

# TRANSLATOR'S NOTE

# TRANSLATOR'S NOTE

# TRANSLATOR'S NOTE

# TRANSLATOR'S NOTE

# INDEX

reversal into its opposite (*Verkehrung*), vii, 96

doubt, colophon of, *see under* subject

drive (*Trieb*), 49

eye, *see under* gaze